Little Hymns • Away In A Manger
Written and illustrated by Andy Holmes
Watercolor by Cameron Thorp and Matt Taylor
Music transcription by Marty Franks

Copyright ©1992 by HSH Educational Media Company
P.O. Box 167187, Irving, Texas 75016

First Printing 1992
ISBN 0-929216-49-0
Printed in the United States of America

Published by

PRESS

Little Hymns™

by Andy Holmes

Away In A Manger

A - way in a man - ger,

no   crib   for   a   bed,

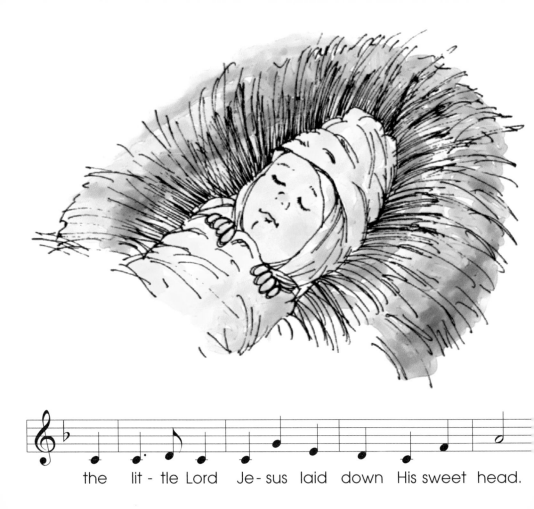

the lit - tle Lord Je - sus laid down His sweet head.

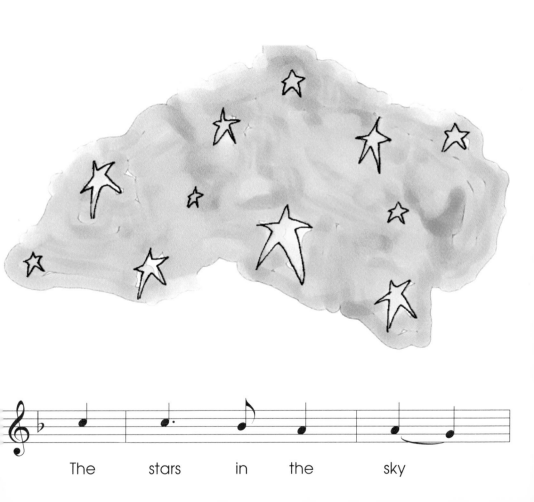

The   stars   in   the   sky

looked   down   where   He   lay,

the   lit - tle Lord   Je - sus, a - sleep on the   hay.

The cat - tle are low - ing,

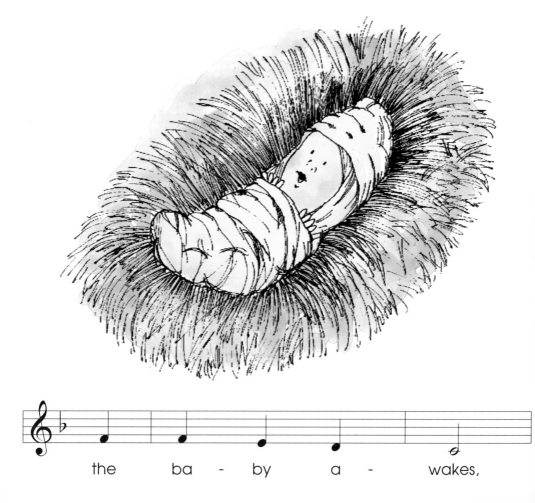

the   ba - by   a -   wakes,

but lit - tle Lord Je - sus, no cry - ing He makes.

I love Thee, Lord Je - sus,

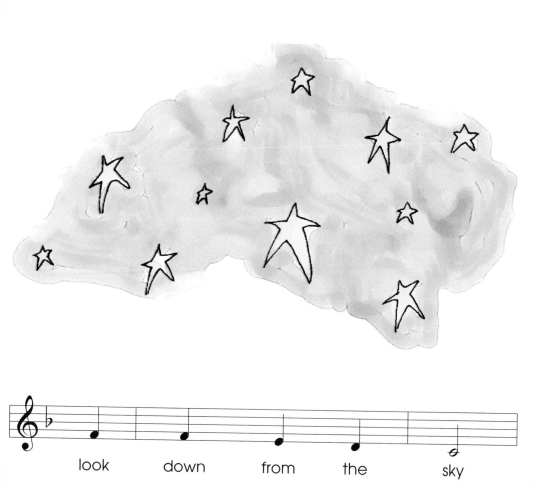

and stay by my cra-dle 'til morn-ing is nigh.

Be near me, Lord Je - sus,

I   ask   Thee   to   stay

close   by   me   for - ev - er,

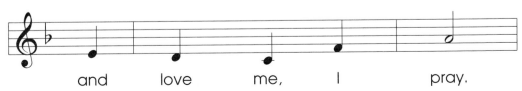

and   love   me,   I   pray.

Bless all the dear chil - dren

in　Thy　ten - der　care,

to   live   with   Thee   there.

Away In A Manger